WILD MUSINGS

ÉANNA NÍ LAMHNA

WILD MUSINGS

A Celebration of the Natural World

Published 2023 by Beehive Books
7–8 Lower Abbey Street, Dublin 1, Ireland
info@beehivebooks.ie
www.beehivebooks.ie

ISBN 978 1 80097 059 5

A catalogue record for this book is available from the British Library.

Photographs
Éanna Ní Lamhna: pp. 34, 40–41, 43, 49, 79, 86, 95.
istockphoto.com: pp. 16–17, 19, 25, 37, 46, 58, 60, 64, 66, 67, 72, 75, 78, 80–81, 92.
Wild Things at School, 2009: 28, 52, 55. Terry Flanagan: pp. 31, 48, 54, 89.
Kevin Hutchinson, Tree Council of Ireland: p. 22. M. Harding: p. 61.

Design & typesetting by Colette Dower, Beehive Books
Cover image: Red squirrel, Éanna Ní Lamhna, *Wild Things at School: A book for
Primary School Teachers*, Meath County Council, 2009
Printed in Ireland by Walsh Colour Print, Kerry

Beehive Books is a member of Publishing Ireland.

*Beehive books are printed on paper made from the wood pulp of managed
forests. For every tree felled, at least one tree is planted, thereby renewing natural
resources.*

For my sister Monica
and my brother Dermot.

Contents

Foreword

Over the last two centuries, humankind's relationship with nature, particularly in the affluent western world, has undergone considerable change. Our empathy for, and our ability to remain in touch with, nature as it weaves its strong, magic, cyclical spells has radically declined. Earlier men and women were born, lived and died in close harmony with the natural world around them: they were an integral part of that world, they spoke its language and lived according to its natural laws. Today, we spend most of our lives in the comfortable, artificial micro-climates of houses, cars or workplaces, and so our experience of the natural world all around us, and even the changing of the seasons, has less and less significance in our everyday lives.

This condition may have led to our lack of awareness about what is happening to our world. The concept of climate change has been discussed and explained by scientists for decades now, but it is only in recent times, through the increase in floods, wildfires and unusually violent storms, that the reality of our situation has begun to dawn on the general populace. We are also learning that it is we ourselves who have brought about this global condition.

Before we can truly back out of the cul-de-sac that the human race has been racing down, and succeed in having any impact on redressing the damage we have done, we must first seriously reconnect with nature. We need to know more about that natural world that we have been out of harmony with for so long, what makes it tick and what makes it sick. We need to be aware of the valuable, inspiring and essentially life-giving treasures of nature that are being needlessly lost, some forever.

Éanna Ní Lamhna is an author, a broadcaster, a botanist and one of the evangelists who has been spreading the word about these issues for years. Through her publications and media appearances she has made the wonderful complexities of ordinary nature fascinating and easy for the lay person to understand and appreciate, firing their imagination and leading inevitably towards a strong realisation that we can benefit from closer harmony with our natural surroundings. In *Wild Musings: A Celebration of the Natural World* Éanna encourages us to become active on behalf of nature, and tells us how we all can help to arrest global warming by getting involved with the natural world, and how we can enjoy and benefit from that involvement. She doesn't pull her punches as she lays out the truly startling facts about how, in spite of the lip service paid by politicians about protecting the climate, the world is continuing blithely down the road towards disaster. We can all help to slow down our lemming-like progress by protecting our local flora and fauna, our local trees, our local birds, even our local patches of wilderness and 'weeds' – places that are now seen as essential habitats. The poet Gerard Manley Hopkins (1844–89) pleaded, in the last verse of his poem 'Inversnaid':

> *What would the world be, once bereft*
> *Of wet and of wildness? Let them be left,*
> *O let them be left, wildness and wet;*
> *Long live the weeds and the wilderness yet.*

Becoming reconnected with nature offers a huge bonus. In the process, we can, without doubt, improve our lives. Research has proven that regular 'connection' with the natural world results in a definite improvement in one's well-being: immersion in the natural world can provide the sure, gentle brake that we all need, and that the world needs too. If we listen to and take to heart the advice of people like Éanna Ní Lamhna, we can enrich our lives and at the same time begin to protect our planet.

Michael Fewer
April 2023

Introduction

Wild Musings is a collection of articles that I wrote in 2021 and 2022 for *Intercom* magazine. The brief was for me to write a series of articles reflecting on the wonder and complexity of our natural world and the dangers that it now faces due to the activities of humankind. So the articles vary between those which describe certain aspects of the world around us, such as butterflies and trees and how hibernation works, and those which explain how our behaviour is causing huge environmental damage. My aim is to maintain a balance between highlighting the importance of action while keeping a positive tone. I explain what people can do to improve our environment.

As a species we are responsible for the state of our planet. How we live affects the world around us. But not only does it affect environmental conditions, it also affects the lives of others in poorer parts of the world. But before we take responsibility for our actions, we first have to understand the implications of what we do. So, my musings, depending on the month when they were written, reflect this. Increasing amounts of carbon dioxide in the air put there over a very short period of time – yes, indeed, two hundred years is a very short time in the existence of our planet – are setting in place a roller coaster of catastrophic climate change. Scientists have been saying this since the 1970s but people chose not to listen, to dismiss such forecasts, until finally in 2022 the impacts were felt even at our own latitudes.

So time is running out for effective action to avert irreversible disaster. It has become a moral issue that must be addressed in order to protect the earth and all living things on it. There is plenty we can do in our own lives: we are not hopeless and helpless. In fact, taking action, even small actions, empowers us and gives us hope and optimism. There is still time – just – for us to turn things around.

My musings ponder how we might do this once we are aware of the absolute necessity for it.

Collectively we made this mess. Collectively we will get out of it.

Ní neart go cur le chéile.

Éanna Ní Lamhna
April 2023

CHAPTER ONE

The World Around Us

Our natural world is changing. We can no longer put our fingers in our ears and pretend not to notice. More floods, droughts, wild fires, etc., are reported every year. What is going on and how can it be sorted out?

Humans are the cleverest species on earth – or so we like to think. Although we are less than one million years on a planet that has had life of some sort for the last 3.5 billion years, we have been a most adaptable and successful species – according to our own standards, that is. (I wonder what whales or pandas make of us or, indeed, what the dodo or the Tasmanian tiger might have to say if somehow we could go back in time and interview them.) There are so many humans now that the earth is creaking at the seams. To keep going, we all really need to know how the world works. It is not enough anymore to leave this to scientists and specialists.

After all, the other species know how the world works and if they get it wrong, they don't last. Survival of the fittest and all that. Hedgehogs that go for a second round of offspring, because it has been a really good summer and there was lots

Two hedgehogs

of food available, find that the youngsters haven't had enough time to put on the required kilogram of fat to tide them over the winter that inexorably follows. Birds that don't build their nests in safe hidden spots well away from the beady eyes of always-watching magpies may lose the whole clutch in a dawn raid. You gotta know what is going on.

Observing how the world works is fascinating. Nothing beats the evidence of your eyes and finding out explanations for it. But in a world where being fobbed off with a mad explanation on social media can have really significant impacts (as opposed

to long ago when fake news meant believing that swans which go missing in summer have turned into beautiful maidens rather than migrated to tundra regions), it is more vital than ever that we all know exactly what is going on and how the natural processes work.

Our planet exists in harmony with the species that inhabit it. While the climate might have been changing slowly over millions of years, the species on it evolved and adapted to these changing conditions. It was only when a calamitous change happened that species extinction was the outcome. We know that this happened 65 million years ago when the planet was struck by a meteorite and the dinosaurs became extinct as their world had changed quicker than they could adapt to it.

The world is changing very quickly at the moment – according to its own terms of reference, as it were. It is heating up exceedingly fast and climatic conditions are affected. This is being caused by one species – humans – who because of their huge numbers and their unsustainable exploitation of the earth's resources are changing the earth's atmosphere so that it traps and retains more of the sun's heat. And this warming is happening in a very short period of time – less than a hundred years. It is calculated that there are less than ten years left at this rate before irreversible change occurs.

We have a beautiful world and we humans are behaving towards it in an irresponsible way. Understanding what is going on is vital for everyone so that the steps needed to sort this out can be taken and supported. We share our world – there are other ways of living besides ours. We do need to understand this. We are only one species and yet so often the attitude to an unrecognised fellow species and sharer of our world is 'what is this and what will it do to me?' Or 'what is this and how do I get rid of it?' It's not all about me, actually – it's all about us all.

If we don't know how the world works, how can we possibly know how to behave in it? By a series of amazing coincidences, planet earth is suitable for living things to exist on. This is so remarkable that, as of yet, in all the galaxies in space that we have discovered, we have not found a single other place where we have detected living things. There are no other planets to which we can migrate when we have banjaxed this one. The mad money being spent travelling to outer space would be much

Planet earth seen from space

better spent keeping this planet habitable for life here. Imagine the terror among living things on some other planet, if such an inhabited one is ever found by us, when they see us coming and learn what we did to our own beautiful Blue Planet.

Viewed from space it is a blue planet because two-thirds of its surface is covered with water. We are the only planet that we know so far that has water and the conditions suitable for retaining it. It plays a vital role in maintaining life on earth. We also have an atmosphere that contains air for us to breathe and some carbon dioxide to keep in some heat rays from the sun so that all the heat the sun sends us isn't just reflected back out into space again.

So, what's the problem then? What's all the hullabaloo about? Well, the thing is that the amount of carbon dioxide in the atmosphere has increased very quickly and is now preventing the escape of more and more reflected heat rays, which causes the temperature of our planet to rise. Reputable and verifiable scientific measurements report that in 1800 the amount was 280 parts per million (ppm) and now it is 415 ppm – gone up by 48 per cent in just over two hundred years, so a lot more heat from the sun is being retained.

Why? Why has the amount of carbon dioxide increased so much in such a short period of time? And is it really the doing of humans?

Yes, well … it is. There is no getting away from the fact that it is humankind's behaviour that has caused the huge increase in atmospheric carbon dioxide. What have we been doing? Two things, actually. First of all, we have been removing the busy carbon-capturing forests. Second, we have been burning fossil fuels and releasing the carbon captured millions of years ago when those deposits of coal, gas and oil were forests. We are putting much more carbon dioxide into the atmosphere and slowing up the mechanism by which it is taken out. And doing it over a very short period of time – as 220 years is in the earth's scale of counting. Elementary, my dear Watson.

We well know what the story is, and there is still time to fix it … but only just. The next ten years is all the time we have to make the big changes that are necessary. The first change is realising this. I will be explaining over the next few chapters how the world works and how what we do impacts on it. You must decide if we humans should continue in this way or not. It is still not too late to change but first we have to truly want to do it.

CHAPTER TWO

Trees –
Good Neighbours of Ours

It was National Tree Day on 6 October 2022 and the theme was 'Trees are Good Neighbours'. They are good neighbours to all the other forms of wildlife who live in them, find food in their leaves, flowers and fruits, and shelter and overwinter in crevices in the bark and roots. Trees are essential for biodiversity, in other words. And they are in their autumn beauty, as the poet W.B. Yeats put it, at this time of year.

But they are good neighbours to us too. In fact, so far, they provide the only way to remove the carbon dioxide in the atmosphere, which is trapping more and more of the sun's heat and causing climate change. Let me explain how exactly trees do this.

Plant an acorn that weighs 20 grams and come back in twenty years' time, and it will have become a tree weighing a tonne. Where did this stuff in the tree come from? The soil? No, because then there would be a big hole under the tree where that material was. The sun? No, because every time a tree grows, a freckle would appear on the face of the sun. The rain? No. The tree is not just 20 grams plus a tonne of water.

Oak tree, Portarlington Golf Club, Co. Laois

So, what's left? The air. Could the tree possibly be made of air? Really? Well, yes, actually it is. A specific part of the air, that is – the carbon part of the carbon dioxide that now forms 415 ppm of our air.

The green leaves of the trees are green because they contain large green molecules called chlorophyll. Light from the sun energises these chlorophyll molecules and enables them, in the presence of water, to split the carbon dioxide molecules in the air apart. The carbon part is captured and taken into the cells of the leaves and the oxygen part is released as a gas which is necessary for animal life. This work, done by the chlorophyll, is called photosynthesis. Without it there could be no life on earth as we know it, and indeed for some billions of years after the formation of planet earth came about, our only form of life here was bacterial, as there was no chlorophyll.

The bigger the plant, the more photosynthesis takes place, so huge plants like trees take a lot of carbon from the air and store it in their bark, branches, leaves and roots. Evergreen trees in warm countries that grow all the year round take in the most. Deciduous trees, such as many of our native trees like oak and ash, only have leaves from May until October so they are off duty for half the year. And evergreen conifers in the northern forests cannot carry out photosynthesis when the temperature is too low. The best rates of carbon capture, or carbon sequestration, to give it its full title, therefore take place in the tropical rainforests – half of which we have already destroyed. Evergreen trees in Ireland capture twice as much carbon as deciduous trees here can. They are able to grow here all the year round as we have mild winters in the world scheme of things and our soils rarely freeze.

So, if we planted lots and lots of trees would we be sorted? How much carbon does each tree actually capture and store? A fast-growing, fairly big tree takes in more than a newly planted sapling can, so here are some figures calculated by considering a fifteen-year-old evergreen Sitka spruce tree (our fastest-growing evergreen), growing in Irish conditions. This fifteen-year-old evergreen tree can remove 20 kg of carbon dioxide from the air in a year and store the carbon as timber. A tonne of timber contains on average the amount of carbon gathered from a tonne of carbon dioxide.

It takes a Sitka spruce forty years to attain maturity, when it could contain five tonnes of timber. This means it has accounted for five tonnes of carbon dioxide during its forty years of growth. Our own native oaks, which are more slow- growing, take at least eighty years to do the same thing. In 2020, the Environmental Protection Agency (EPA) calculated that Ireland emitted 57.7 million tonnes of carbon dioxide into the atmosphere that year. Planting trees to absorb that amount of carbon would mean thirty thousand hectares tied up for forty years growing fast-growing conifers at a mature size of 400 trees per hectare, just to offset one year's carbon dioxide emissions. Given that we only have 7 million hectares of land in the entire country, planting it all with trees would only offset a finite number of years of emissions, which is not practicable. Apart from the small matter of where we might live and how we might grow crops and food, all of the country is not suited for growing trees anyway.

Mind you, we could plant some more than we have already, as we currently have only 11 per cent of the country covered with trees – well below the EU average of 42 per cent. But the fact remains, there is no way we can ever remove all the carbon

Forest surrounding Muckross Abbey, Killarney, Co. Kerry

dioxide we emit into the atmosphere by planting trees and keeping them going for at least forty years.

Carbon sinks might help. What exactly is a carbon sink? Well, it is not some new-fangled must-have you need to acquire the next time you are doing up your kitchen. It is a store of carbon that has been put beyond use – decommissioned, as it were. A carbon sink holds on to carbon in such a way that it cannot escape, unite with oxygen atoms and make a bolt for the atmosphere in the form of heat-holding carbon dioxide gas. There are actually only two ways that carbon can become part of a carbon dioxide molecule. One of these ways is by burning, when the carbon molecule unites with oxygen, whether that process is in the car engine, in a fireplace or in a runaway forest fire. The other way it gets there is through the decomposition process – when dead plants and trees are broken down by microorganisms such as bacteria and fungi.

If things are too wet, they won't burn. If they are very acidic and lack any oxygen, the decomposing microorganisms cannot live there. Which is why bogs, made from sphagnum mosses that grew and captured carbon from the air over the last thousands of years in Ireland, are such splendid carbon sinks. At the maximum, 15.5 per cent of the whole country was covered with bogs, so it is easy to see what an important carbon sink Irish bogs once were – and indeed still are, although they have been greatly reduced by cutting and burning turf.

Soil can contain lots of carbon from plants that grew there and whose remains are still in the soil – particularly peaty soils. Coal deposits and those of oil and natural gas are all carbon sinks as well – as long as they stay where they are and are not removed and burnt as fuel.

So you can see how we can all do our bit by being good neighbours to trees: we can plant more of them (or have them planted for us if we have no space). And we can understand why burning fossil fuels, which essentially means destroying carbon sinks, increases the rate of climate change. Using electricity instead – electricity made from renewable sources such as wind and sun – is the way we have to go, as quickly as possible.

CHAPTER THREE

Surviving the Winter

'For now the winter is past, the rain is over and gone.
The flowers appear on the earth; the time of singing has
come, and the voice of the turtle-dove is heard in our land.'
(Song of Solomon 2:11-12)

The first of February is the first day of spring, St Brigid's Day. As the poet Antoine Ó Raifteirí (Anthony Raftery) said:

Anois teacht an Earraigh
Beidh an lá dul chun shíneadh
Is tar éis na Féile Bhríde
Ardóigh mé mo sheol.

And as the days continue to lengthen, although it mightn't necessarily be getting warmer, there is a sense of relief that we 'didn't die a winter yet' and have another year to look forward to. The longer daylight hours activate the production of more serotonin in our brains, helping us to have a positive approach for the days ahead.

Red squirrel

Surviving winter can be very difficult for wildlife too. Food is scarce and more energy is needed to keep warm than is required during the warmer part of the year. So those that can, follow the warmer weather. It's easy for birds; they can fly off to hotter climes as they do in their annual migrations. But what about mammals whose food supplies vanish when the colder weather comes? What are they supposed to do? One wonderful and successful strategy is to sleep it out for the winter and wake up when the good times come again.

It does sound like a good idea on a cold dark November evening when the clocks have gone back and it is dark by 4.00 p.m. It will be like this till the end of January at least. Couldn't we humans hibernate too? We could reschedule Christmas, after all. But the thing is, if we went to sleep in mid-November and didn't wake up until February, we would not wake up. We would have died of hunger and thirst. So how do creatures like the hedgehog survive this hibernation?

The trick is that the hedgehog is able to slow its metabolic rate when in hibernation and so its fat reserves last all winter. Normally hedgehogs – which are small animals – have a heartbeat of about 200 beats per minute, they have a body temperature of around 40°C and breathe about fifteen times per minute. They need lots of food to maintain this high metabolic rate and so are hungry hunters of snails and slugs, to the delight of gardeners. However, when they are in hibernation, hedgehogs' heartbeat reduce to one per minute, their temperature drops to 10°C and they breathe once every three minutes. It takes a lot less fuel to maintain this very low metabolic rate. If they have increased their fat stores so that they weigh at least one kilogram before they go into hibernation, and no nasty event causes them to wake up during winter, they will last until April. Mind you, they will be very hungry when they wake up. The squashed corpses of hedgehogs that we sometimes see on the roads at the end of April are testimony to their desperate forays looking for food. Helpful bowls of dog food in the garden can be very welcome to them at this time.

We humans cannot slow down our metabolic rate so that we barely tick over. We can last a night but generally most of us are quite happy to have breakfast the next day (and two further meals, if we can lay our hands on them). A heartbeat of sixty beats per minute and a temperature of 37°C, even when we are asleep, requires a lot of energy, which regular eating provides us with. So, no hibernation for us then.

And what about the squirrel? Those of us who learn our science from story books are convinced that squirrels hibernate. Think about it. What do they do in autumn? They gather great supplies of nuts and store them away. The very verb – to squirrel something away – reflects this. They are good at collecting and storing supplies of food. Therefore, is it likely that having done all this hard work they would then go and hibernate for the winter? By the time they woke up in April the nuts would have germinated and grown into trees!

Squirrels are not eejits. They collect stores of food that will keep because they are going to be awake and eating them over the winter months. They each have to fend for themselves. There are no dig-outs in the world of nature.

Mammals are not the only creatures that hibernate to survive the winter. Other groups do it too – cold-blooded animals whose body temperatures are regulated by the environment rather than by the energy created by digesting large quantities

Hedgehog, garden in Clonsilla, Dublin

of food. So cold-blooded creatures in surroundings where temperatures are very low for part of the year hibernate when it is too cold to function. Our amphibians, the frogs, newts and natterjack toads, and our reptiles, the viviparous lizard and the slow-worm, all hibernate during the winter when it is too cold for them to move and there is no food available for them either as they are all carnivores, depending on insects for food.

Invertebrates – animals without backbones – are all cold-blooded creatures so they have differing strategies to survive winter. Some hibernate, such as the snails who seal off the undersides of their shells once they have reached the safety of large clumps of overhanging ivy or some such safe place and can spend the winter there.

The wasps, bumble bees and bluebottle flies hibernate only as fertilised queens. They have already safely gone away after mating in August to a secure place to spend the winter fast asleep. Most butterflies hibernate in the chrysalis (or cocoon) stage of their life cycle and emerge as adults when temperatures rise again. There are a few exceptions, such as the small tortoiseshell butterfly, that orange one with the blue spots around the bottom of its back wings; these hibernate as adults, inside our houses in the curtains of the good parlour if we let them. Honeybees, of course, don't hibernate at all. They were originally a tropical species, coming from a region where hibernation is not necessary. They store great supplies of honey to use as food when flowers full of nectar are in short supply, and they all cluster around their queen to keep her warm. We meanly take some of their honey for ourselves. In fact, this ability to make and store big quantities of honey is the reason why humankind domesticated them in the first place, honey being the earliest source of concentrated sweetness in these latitudes.

So, hibernation works as a survival strategy. We can look forward to seeing all these creatures again when the temperatures are high enough to wake them up from their slumbers which never happens on 1 February, no matter what we are told about groundhogs in America!

And together with looking out for the first swallows back from Africa and spotting the first primroses on a sunny bank, the prospect of getting out of doors is really attractive. As the poet Tennyson said,

> *In the Spring a young man's fancy lightly turns to thoughts of love.*

You don't have to be young – or a tree – for spring to really gladden your heart.

CHAPTER FOUR

Our Warming World

The latest reports from scientists tell us that the last ten years have been the warmest on record, with 2020 being on average 1.3 degrees celsius above pre-industrial levels two hundred years ago. This is because of the continued impact of human-induced climate change on our global climate. For the last fifty years, our global climate has been warming by about 0.2°C each decade. This underlying warming, due primarily to our use of coal, oil and gas – fossil fuels – is what matters for monitoring climate change and tracking our progress against the goals of the Paris Agreement, more so than the warmth of any individual year. Nevertheless, it is notable that we have just experienced, globally, the second-warmest year of the warmest decade on record.

The Paris Agreement was a legally binding international agreement on climate change that was adopted by 196 countries at COP21 in Paris in December 2015. But signing an agreement is one thing, putting it into practice is another. We know things must be getting worse because the newspapers and other media are now taking it seriously and reporting on it much more. We all know about COP26 held in Glasgow in November 2021. The

Giant beech tree, University College Dublin, Belfield, Dublin

first day was taken up with presidents and princes and film stars and *taoisigh* all appearing in person in Glasgow to speak for their allotted three minutes. They talked about how seriously they were taking this and pledged their own and their country's commitment to taking immediate steps to having the issue resolved by 2050 and indeed half-resolved by 2030.

The amount of fossil fuel burnt in the jet returning from Glasgow to Washington emitted 590 kg of carbon dioxide greenhouse gas into the atmosphere per passenger. This is what one Irish person causes to be emitted in seven weeks or – think of this – what four people in Uganda or Somalia together would cause to be emitted in a whole year. And these African countries are the ones hardest hit by famines caused by the increasing droughts that climate change is bringing. But planting trees will mitigate this – right?

Trees take in carbon dioxide from the air as they grow and store it in the timber in their trunks. Evergreen trees have leaves all year round and can grow continuously if the temperature stays even a little above freezing. Deciduous trees only have leaves for six months – from late April to late October – and only take in carbon dioxide from the air during these six months. So, for each person on that presidential flight back to Washington (and I am sure it wasn't as packed as regular passenger planes), it would have needed at least fifty decent-sized ten-year-old evergreen trees growing for a whole year or one hundred ten-year-old oak trees similarly busy for the year, to remove the climate-changing gas produced on just that one trip home from COP26. I am sure that many of the other heads of state who pledged their allegiance to halting climate change flew there too on a fossil-fuel-burning aircraft.

But is it a case of – in the words of St Augustine – 'make me pure, but not yet!'? It's one thing to promise the divil and all on a world stage in Glasgow and quite another to sell the changes required to a reluctant population at home upon whom you depend for re-election. We really all have to be convinced that this is a threat to the very existence of our planet and that we are all in this together. And I am not referring to COVID-19.

In Ireland, electricity was traditionally produced by burning fossil fuels such as coal, turf, oil and natural gas to boil the water to make the steam to turn the turbines. In 1990, according to the Environmental Protection Agency (EPA), fully 21 per cent of our greenhouse gas emissions came from the energy generation sector. Since then, generating electricity by harnessing the wind to turn the turbines has become possible. Electricity produced in this way causes no carbon dioxide greenhouse gas to be emitted into the atmosphere. In 1990, 21 per cent of our greenhouse gas emissions came from this energy generation sector. In 2020, despite the fact that we have a larger population and more demand, this had fallen to 15 per cent of our emissions for that year.

This is because we are getting more and more clean electricity from the wind – 13.5 per cent during 2020. We have lots and lots of wind in Ireland, both overland and offshore. We could be harnessing much more of it to generate more clean electricity, which could be used to heat our houses instead of coal, oil or gas, or drive our cars instead of petrol or diesel. And indeed that is the plan. There are all sorts of targets set for 2030 and even more ambitious ones set for 2050. The politicians have no problem signing up to international agreements and publicly stating how much they support these initiatives.

Wildflowers

But they won't work if the population of the country isn't behind the initiatives and seeing them as a good idea rather than political manoeuvring. As of early January 2021, 77 per cent of the whole population – adults and children (and these numbers have continued to rise) – were fully vaccinated against COVID-19 because they saw the vaccine as saving them from an immediate danger that affected their health. But somehow, many of us don't see that more generators, safely erected to the highest standards in windy places, are a very effective means of reducing our greenhouse gas emissions. We don't like the look of them. They ruin the view. Put them somewhere else.

And of course, there is always the argument that someone is sure to trot out, that Ireland with a population of only 5 million or so emits only a tiny percentage on a world scale. Actually, Ireland as a country emits as much greenhouse gas annually as do Eritrea, Rwanda, Burundi, Sierra Leone and Malawi put together: over 55 million people. And these countries are really suffering from climate change with droughts, water shortages and crop failures. Each and every one of us emitted 6.75 tonnes of greenhouse gases in 2020. No country in Africa except for South Africa and Libya, both with 7.2 tonnes per head, came anywhere close to this. In the EU, only Poland and Germany are worse than us. So per capita we are major world polluters.

Treading more lightly on the earth is essential. Knowing our impact is the first step. Every little does actually help. Small little Ireland was the first country to charge for plastic bags. It was the first country to ban smoking indoors in public places. These practices are widespread now in other countries and we showed the way because we thought it was a good idea. We have to think that making changes to slow down global warming is a good idea too rather than dismissing it as political carry-on that we cannot afford. The lives of our children and our grandchildren really do depend on it.

There is still time this year to plant a tree (or ten) and to lobby against the ridiculous requirement that planting permission is required to plant more than one hectare with trees. There is still time to walk or cycle and to lobby for more public transport and safer routes for pedestrians and cyclists. There is still time to do away with all these ridiculous lawns that require the use of huge amounts of fossil fuels to mow them each week and replace them with wildflower meadows that bees and other pollinators will thank you for. There is still time to arrange a summer holiday that does not involve an air journey. It is not too late − yet.

CHAPTER FIVE

The Importance of the Commons

'[T]hose who believed ...
everything they owned was held in common.'
(Acts 4:32)

Owning things in common is a concept that is very familiar to those Irish people who grazed animals on commonage – whether this was mountainside or sand-dune grasslands. Each farmer put out his animals, marked with a distinctive dye, and they grazed freely without fences or boundaries. The sheepdog rounded them up at the times of the year that shearing, dipping or indeed selling happened. There was a balance; there had to be. No point in putting out more animals than could thrive on the vegetation that grew there. The carrying capacity of the commonage was appreciated and respected – farmers, after all, had to make a living from the weight gain of their animals.

In the 1980s, however, that link was broken by EU grants. The French, in particular, couldn't get enough of Irish lamb, so headage grants were paid to farmers to keep more sheep. They were paid by the number of sheep presented for counting when

Great Blasket Island, Co. Kerry

the inspector called. It didn't matter if they were merely bags of bones or would never have enough meat to grace a French dinner table. It was a headage payment, it was the number of sheep that mattered. The Irish national sheep herd increased from 3.3 million in 1980 to 8.5 million by 1990. Numbers stayed above 8 million for the whole of the 1990s. The commonage grazing areas hadn't got any bigger, but the number of animals grazing there had increased spectacularly. Not only was all the grass eaten away, but the heather, which sheep only eat when grass is not available, was eaten away too. There was no vegetation left to hold the thin mountain soils in place and huge amounts of soil erosion occurred, destroying these fragile habitats. The carrying capacity of the commonage had been greatly exceeded

because the link with nature had been broken by the headage payments. These were stopped in the end but the long-term environmental damage was done. Sheep numbers in 2020 were back to 3.8 million. It is going to take a lot longer for those eroded mountainsides to recover – if indeed they ever do.

We have other commons too. The air we breathe is held in common by us all. Polluted air, caused by human activity, takes its toll on our health. The latest EPA report tells us that 1,300 people die premature deaths in Ireland every year because of the domestic burning of smoky solid fuel. Only smokeless coal may be burnt by law in our cities, but there is resistance to this requirement being expanded to cover the whole of the country, even though it is for the common good. Our air is a resource we all hold in common, so is this resistance fair?

Clean water is another resource we all hold in common. Our drinking supplies do not come from the rain directly. The rain either runs off the land into rivers and lakes or sinks through the soil into aquifers which are accessed via wells. Local authorities have to clean the water they take in before they can send it out to our houses in the water supply. People not so supplied have to use, and pay for, group water schemes or else use their own private wells and hope for the best. What is spread on and below the soil affects our water quality. We have around half a million septic tanks discharging into the subsoil and trickling down into the water table. Whether this contains harmful bacteria injurious to our heath depends on how well the tank is maintained. Properly managed septic tanks will not cause pollution. What is sprayed on our fields can run off into waterbodies and affect the water quality there. There are regulations to mitigate against all this – spraying times, septic tank registration and maintenance, inspection requirements and so on. Flouting these means that poisons and nasty bacteria can pollute the lakes and rivers and the water held in the aquifers below ground. These are a resource we all hold in common, and the regulations are there to protect this common good.

However, with our population of 5 million, we have not exceeded the carrying capacity of these commons. We don't actually have to have any dirty air and water – if everyone realises the impact of what they do and appreciates the protective legislation that is there. Other countries with much larger and fast-growing populations are not so lucky. Air and water pollution leads to 10 million deaths per year on a world-wide basis, particularly in parts of the world where the dense population has exceeded the local carrying capacity.

Diamond Hill, Co. Galway

Air and water and indeed mountainsides are not the only commons. Oceans, forests, icecaps, etc. are commons too and there is a finite amount of them on planet earth. The world's population is now eight billion. We all need clean air to breathe, clean water for our needs and enough food to eat. Are we entitled to over-use and pollute these at the expense of others we share the world with?

We need places to live too and places to dispose of our waste. Waste? Humans are the only ones who produce waste. Animals in the wild don't. Their droppings are naturally biodegraded, and the nutrients contained restore fertility so that new food can grow. It is true that too many animals contained in one area, however, produce more waste than the earth's natural processes can deal with and this can lead to water pollution if not managed properly. But this is hardly their fault and at least they don't drink water out of plastic bottles and then throw them away. In general, the wealthier humans are, the more waste they produce.

There are much fewer carnivores than herbivores in the natural world. This is quite easy to understand when we realise that all the food on earth is made by plants in the first instance. Feeding on plants, which is what herbivores do, directly accesses this food. Eating the animals that eat the plants is what carnivores do – the next step up in the food chain that we learned about in school. Each level in the food chain only contains 10 per cent of the energy contained in the level beneath it, which is why so much land must be cleared of forest to raise cattle for us to eat as beef. The same land under crops would feed ten times as many people.

If the world's population continues to rise, it is inevitable that eventually the carrying capacity of our planet will be exceeded. This will happen sooner if the lifestyle of some of these billions means they continue to overuse and pollute the earth's resources. This is the tragedy of the commons and it's not fair or just or sustainable.

It is not inevitable, though, if we can learn to share equitably, and tread lighter on the earth.

CHAPTER SIX

Becoming Nature Positive

The year 2022 has not been a happy year so far. World events such as disease and war have brought much grief and hardship. I find that there is always one thing that gives me an unequivocal feeling of progress, hope and optimism for the future, and that is our natural world. The summer season is starting again as it always does every year. Nature follows the order of things and knowing this lifts the spirit. By focusing on the animals, plants, fungi and the environments around us, we uncover a multidimensional world of wonder. It can be uplifting to focus on nature positivity and conservation optimism. Being nature positive means believing that conservation actions can work, nature recovery is possible and ambitious goals at the global scale can motivate the action that we need. We do need to feel that we have some control over what goes on around us. Young people in particular are more prone to being pessimistic about the future of our natural world and this leads to depression. So let us start the summer by being nature positive.

There are five ways to be nature positive. The first is to go outdoors and experience nature. The return of longer days helps

Bumblebee on lavender

us to appreciate the role of nature in regulating our mood and improving mental health. There is the '1,000 Hours Outside' movement, which advocates the value of spending time in nature. Research shows that just an hour or two a week in nature is beneficial for people's well-being. If the three hours a day needed for one thousand hours a year is a bit steep, rest assured that just getting out for thirty minutes a day can give you a nature boost. Many of us have been doing just that during the pandemic lockdowns of 2020 and 2021. It is a good habit to continue.

The second way is to protect the nature around you. When you are outdoors and notice what wildlife likes and where you can see it, the next step is to see if you can make the circumstances more favourable for it. That tatty bit of the garden with long grass and weeds, which of course are actually wildflowers, could be a wildlife haven for hedgehogs, pollinators and birds. So, take a break from the lawnmower or at the very least only mow every six weeks and enjoy the dandelions and daisies on your lawn, not to speak of the other small flowers that appear when mowing stops – self-heal, speedwell, buttercup, clover – all manner of flowers. Don't use weedkillers or put down blue pellets for slugs. You are actively killing wildlife by doing this and introducing poisons into the environment. A bit of hand weeding, if necessary, or a band of copper tape around your favourite potted plants should do the trick in a much more sustainable way.

The third thing to do is to get involved with groups that work for nature recovery. There are thousands of volunteers around the country doing brilliant work for nature including your local Tidy Towns group, most of whom have signed up to the All-Ireland Pollinator Plan. Many of these groups work locally so

Robin's pincushion (scabious)

there are opportunities to meet new people, to spend time in nature, to get fit and to help with a large positive project for the environment. Small local actions that yield results very often lead to bigger actions. Working with like-minded people can increase our own satisfaction with what we are doing and make us more likely to stick at it. Joining groups such as Birdwatch Ireland gets you out, if you go on their fieldtrips, teaches you about the birds you see and provides you with interesting reading material both through their magazines and their website.

The fourth way of becoming nature positive is to find out more about nature. For example, until you learn that there is more than one species of moss on a wall, all you see is a sea of green. As you learn more and more species, that sea of green resolves into a complex weave of many shades, textures and shapes. Watching what wildflowers appear on your unmowed lawn and what insects visit them makes even looking out your window a learning experience. Being able to recognise ten different species of cliff-nesting seabirds when you look at a summer breeding colony on a noisy cliff face through binoculars is indeed an incomparable experience. On miserable wet days when going out is not on, you can learn still learn about nature from the comfort of your own home. Research has shown that watching natural history films sparks a big upsurge in interest in the species featured.

Speedwell – a flower of unmowed lawns, Terenure, Dublin

And, of course, share what you have learnt with others. The fifth step involves talking about nature with friends and family. Talk to your local representatives too and say what you would like to see done locally, nationally and internationally to enable more people to get benefits from nature. If you have been following steps one to four, you will be very informed about your local area's wildlife and what you would like to see done to improve it. Nature needs advocates to bring its many values to the table where decisions are made. Politicians often split the world into 'doorstep issues' which they feel get them elected and 'non-doorstep issues' which they feel people don't really care about day to day. We need to make nature a 'doorstep issue'. How is your area for trees? Could more be planted? What state is the local river in? It should be a wonderful amenity for both wildlife and for the humans who like to walk along its banks. What is your local park like and how is it managed? Many local authorities are easing off on mowing and spraying in order for wildlife to benefit. Is this the case in your local park? Or is there even a local park at all? Positive interaction and suggestions always go down better than criticism.

So, in order to feel better in a world that sometimes seems to have gone mad and be out of control, having conservation optimism and being nature positive is a goal to pursue.

CHAPTER SEVEN

Butterflies – Nature's Flying Flowers

It's June, it's high summer and nature is looking its best. The trees are in leaf – lovely fresh leaves – and many are in flower too, or have just finished flowering. The birds are busy – very busy indeed – feeding their young. Males are protecting their territories and their mates with loud birdsong, proclaiming that they are king in their own patch and then assiduously helping the missus with the task of food collecting for the ever-hungry growing youngsters. There is a riot of flowers, which are visited by insects on the hunt for nectar, and indeed for pollen too, in the case of the bees.

Butterflies are particularly evident now, flying around in any sunshine that occurs. Gardens, hedgerows, wildflower meadows and roadside verges are really important refuges for them. A good garden with the right food plants could well contain up to nineteen of our thirty-five butterfly species. Adult butterflies have been on the wing since the end of March and, depending on species, can be seen flying until the start of November. They do all their feeding as caterpillars usually on specific plants – not just any old leaf. Then they go into a cocoon within which

Cabbage white butterfly on buddleia

they are transformed. All the caterpillar cells are rearranged so that a beautiful insect with four brightly coloured wings is formed. Then the cocoon bursts open and the glorious butterfly emerges.

Adults have but one aim in life. They need to meet another butterfly of the same species but opposite gender, in order to mate and lay eggs. Their whole body is designed for this. They no longer eat. They have no intestines and they do not excrete. They get most of their energy from the food they ate as caterpillars. But they top up their energy levels with sweet drinks – the pubs that supply these are nectar-rich flowers. Butterflies have a hollow tube called a proboscis for sucking up this nectar.

Some flowers are much more suitable for them than others. The proper nectar-rich flowering plants and shrubs, particularly in a sunny, sheltered part of the garden, will attract a veritable host of butterflies on a warm sunny day.

They can drink from any flower in which the nectar is accessible; it is only for egg-laying that they need a particular plant species. So on a warm sunny day in June you could see several different species on the same buddleia bush – like a singles bar, as it were. In open countryside, flower-rich grasslands are particularly important too. A pity that so many of these continue to be replaced by single grass species, closely mown, silage fields that are no good for any of our native wildlife.

Although we have only 35 native species of butterfly, which is a small number when you consider that the total for the EU as a whole is 450, we have a good variety of colour among them. Gardeners are well familiar with the white ones, some species of which depend on brassicas such as the best cabbage or cauliflower for their caterpillars to feed on. But there are elegant fluttering wood whites too that you may encounter in sunny glades on your woodland walk.

The original butterfly in these parts is the brimstone. This big yellow butterfly is particularly evident in May. The really brightly coloured males can fly long distances looking for females. Long ago, May was the great growing season for grass and the cows out to pasture were able now to produce good quantities of milk. There was enough to spare to set it aside for the cream to rise and be collected for butter making. And this yellow brimstone was always on the wing when the butter making started. So what else would you call this creature, the same colour as butter, that appeared around now, only a butterfly? Its name in other

Male holly blue butterfly

languages does not reflect this. In Greek the word is psyche, which means soul. This interpretation is found in other cultures too. The Latin name for the whole group – *lepidoptera* – means scale wings, as the colour on butterfly wings is reflected from the scales there. Old butterflies are dull in colour as they have lost many of their scales.

Our rainbow of butterfly colours includes blue. The richly coloured holly blue flies in gardens where holly and ivy grow as these are the plant foods for the caterpillars. You will see green butterflies – the tiny green hairstreaks – on our bogs, as the females lay their eggs on heather. Lose the bogs and this species will become extinct.

Fields covered with buttercups are often a veritable feast for the eye, with clouds of meadow brown butterflies in early June. This is our most common butterfly, brown all over with orange patches on the forewings. But there are some species that are not content with being just one or two colours. The peacock butterfly really does live up to its name. It has magnificent red wings with four large blue eye spots. Yet when it lands and closes its wings, it seems to vanish as the undersides of all four wings are dull black. It lays its eggs on the common stinging nettle, as indeed do at least four other butterfly species in this

Peacock butterfly

group including the elegant summer visitor – the black, red and white red admiral. You will be well repaid if you leave a small patch of nettles in a disused corner of the garden as this whole group of butterflies really do look like flying flowers.

So, what else could you have growing in the garden to improve the number of butterfly species that come to visit? Everyone knows that *Buddleja davidii* is also known as the butterfly bush, but butterflies are very fond of hebe too, as well as hawthorn, Guelder-rose and honeysuckle. Plants such as lavender, verbena and grape hyacinth will amply repay the space they occupy with lots of visiting pollinating species on the hunt for nectar, not just butterflies. You may have decided to turn some of your lawn into a wildflower meadow to cut down on the amount of senseless grass mowing and to provide for bees, but many species of butterfly will be attracted here too. You can augment whatever emerged naturally when you stop mowing, with scabious (pincushion plants) and knapweed, bird's foot trefoil, red clover and cowslips.

So it is really all of a piece. Growing lovely garden flowers and wildflowers provides lots of pleasure in itself. But when such lovely creatures as butterflies come to nectar-swigging parties there as well on lovely sunny summer days, then the whole uplifting effect of nature in harmony really is unbeatable. And did I mention the melodious birdsong, and the exquisite fragrance of the lavender or the gorse being visited? Be sure to engage all your senses.

After all this, don't forget to keep an account of the butterflies you see and send your findings to Butterfly Conservation Ireland at www.butterflyconservation.ie.

CHAPTER EIGHT

Called After the Saints – What's in a Name?

St George's mushroom, St Mark's fly and St John's wort are some of the species of wildlife that have saints' names. Why are they so called? Were these saints into wildlife? Was mycology or entomology or botany their particular speciality?

No, it is much simpler than that. These species were called after these particular saints because they appeared on that saint's day. Of course, people long ago were much more knowledgeable about feast days than they are today. In fact, if you stopped people on the street they would be hard pressed to tell you who St George was (a Turk, apparently) never mind being able to state when his feast day is. It is on 23 April and on that day St George's mushrooms begin to appear. These are white mushrooms with whitish gills and their habitat is roadsides, pastures and grassland. It used to grow at home in the grass in our front garden in Co. Louth and probably still does. But the interesting thing about this mushroom is how early it appears. Most mushrooms appear in late summer and early autumn. This one so regularly appeared at the end of April on St George's feast day that it was called after the saint. True to form this year, it

Wren

turned up at the end of April and was noticed in the many grassy areas that were left unmowed so that there were wildflowers for the bees.

And what about St Mark's fly? This is quite a large, day-flying, black, hairy insect which hangs about in groups soaking up the sun, as it were. They attract attention from us because they look as if they have a big long sting coming out of their underside. This is just their legs, which they hold together under their body as they hover in the air. And what is going on is that this is a swarm of male flies on the pull. They are hanging around looking for females which are sitting on the grass below. When the females see them and fly up to join them they are seized peremptorily by the males who promptly mate with them then and there in the air. I wonder what St Mark makes of it all? The flies were also on time this year. St Mark's Day was 25 April. I saw loads of them when I was hillwalking on Bray Head on the May bank holiday Monday. They are usually around for a couple of weeks.

St John's Day (called after St John the Baptist) is on 24 June. This day – or more particularly St John's Eve – was always quite special because 24 June was considered to be Midsummer's Day. I remember my uncle in Donegal lighting a bonfire on St John's Eve as had always been the tradition. Cattle were driven through the flames to protect them from disease. The flames would certainly dislodge any ticks that might be burrowing into the cattle so maybe it did work. There are several species of St John's wort, which is a yellow flower with five petals. They were traditionally considered to have been given special properties by St John. Making tea from its leaves was said to be good for your nerves. In fact, the species does actually have medicinal

St Patrick's cabbage

properties – quite potent ones too – and people taking modern medicines are advised to stay away from St John's wort as it may well react badly with conventional medicine. There are ten or eleven different species of St John's wort in Ireland and most of them are in flower by the end of June.

St Dabeoc's heath is a pinkish, purplish heather that only occurs in west Galway and west Mayo, so nowhere else in Ireland, or indeed in Britain. It is also native to Spain and Portugal, but it was the Irish specimens that were first described scientifically in the 1700s and they kept their local name. But who was St Dabeoc and why was this rare heather called after him? He was a disciple of St Patrick and is credited with founding a monastery on an island in Lough Derg in Co. Donegal that is a place of pilgrimage to this day. He must have visited Mayo and Galway too and blessed this heather because carrying it on your person was considered to ward off incontinence. It flowers from June to August so St Dabeoc's feast day must fall in those months.

And St Patrick wasn't behind the door in having a plant called after him. St Patrick's cabbage is not a cabbage at all but a wildflower – one of the saxifrage family. It occurs in shady, wet areas in the west and south-west. It produces small pinky-white flowers from May to July – long after St Patrick's Day. It doesn't occur in Britain either – it is another member of our Lusitanian flora, turning up again only in Spain and Portugal. It is not credited with being a cure for anything, so maybe it is called after St Patrick to show its distinct Irishness – although would people long ago have known of its absence in Britain? Maybe it does cure something?

St George's mushroom, Stillorgan, Co. Dublin

However, the saints don't seem to have spent too much time birdwatching. While St Stephen is associated with the wren and St Brigid with the oystercatcher, there is no Irish bird whose name incorporates a saint's name – or is there? St Stephen was betrayed by a wren who danced on the drum of a group of sleeping Roman soldiers and woke them up as Stephen, an early Christian, was sneaking past them. He was duly caught and executed – the first martyr – and is honoured by having his feast day the very next day after Christmas. Hence the custom of wren boys who traditionally hunted and killed wrens on this day to punish the wren for his betrayal of Stephen. Such activity is of course illegal now, so the rites of the wren boys nowadays are confined to singing.

St Brigid is associated with the oystercatcher – a black and white wading shorebird with red legs. The Irish name for this bird – just in Connacht – is *Giolla Bríghde*, St Brigid's servant. The story is that a flock of oystercatchers once saved St Brigid from being pursued by covering her with seaweed. Handy lads to have around all right.

There are probably lots of names associated with local wildlife which are just local names. These names were given in simpler times when knowledge of local saints and indeed the holy wells associated with them were part of local folklore and tradition. So it is nice to see that at least some of them live on in their names to this day.

CHAPTER NINE

What Do We Know About Wildlife – Do We Really Care?

I have been talking, writing and teaching about wildlife my whole life. The people I communicate with seem interested in learning about what is around them, and wildlife books and radio and television programmes are quite popular too. So, you can imagine my amazement when I read the results of a recent survey carried out in Britain by Redrow, which asked two thousand adults, all of whom have gardens, about their knowledge of wildlife. The results seemed to me to be quite appalling. Apparently 42 per cent of these people cannot identify a robin correctly and 14 per cent cannot say, when presented with two images, which one is a magpie and which one is a blackbird. A quarter of those surveyed had no idea that a caterpillar turns into a butterfly in due course while more than half, 55 per cent, actually, couldn't tell the difference between a butterfly and a moth. And these are the people who have gardens and care for them. What must the rest of them be like?

However, what is even more dispiriting is the realisation that all these people are not interested enough in the creatures that visit their gardens to find out what they are. People can list all

Robin

the players that ever scored for their favourite football team or know the make of any car they see on the street because they are interested in them. Why don't they have an interest in the wildlife they share their garden with?

Could we be the same here? Certainly, the first question I am usually asked when being interviewed is 'when did you become interested in wildlife?' As if this was some sort of unusual interest and that I took it up at a certain stage in my life. I usually retort that everyone starts off by being fascinated by the wildlife around us and that it is the adults in children's lives who teach them to be afraid of spiders or deter them from playing with worms or snails. Children have a wonderful curiosity that adults can diminish, in the same way as their own curiosity was stamped out in earlier times.

But would a survey of two thousand Irish adults produce the same results, I wonder? Our educational system nowadays cannot be blamed anyway. Biology has been a Leaving Cert subject since 1971. Environmental studies have been on the primary school curriculum since the 1970s too and it was greatly improved in 1999 when the social, environmental and scientific module was developed. We are the best country in the world for Green Flags in schools, with almost 90 per cent of our schools proudly flying a green flag that took two years of hard work to achieve, and involved learning about energy use, or water quality, or biodiversity, or whichever of the current ten themes that flags are awarded for. Their parents are involved too and their awareness increases as well.

It's vital to have at least a little understanding of what's happening in our gardens. The more we learn and understand, the more we can help the wildlife around us thrive. Our

Blackbird

government declared a biodiversity emergency in 2019 that was caused by the lack of space and habitats for wildlife because of land-use change. We have the second iteration of the All-Ireland Pollinator Plan covering 2021–25. Local authorities, Tidy Towns groups and gardeners are all easing up on the mowing of grassy areas and letting wildflowers grow. Surely we are more knowledgeable and care more than our friends across the water?

And yet I have lost count of the areas of roadside verges outside people's homes that have been sprayed with weed killer, leading to an unsightly strip of dead yellow vegetation where nothing can live, including the creatures in the soil beneath.

How could anyone decide that this poisoned verge outside their house is a good idea? And I have crossed verbal swords with some who think unmowed roundabouts full of wildflowers or unmowed strips in public parks are somehow really slacking and money-saving exercises by local authorities, and that tight mowing by machines that burn fossil fuels should be brought back at once.

The EU banned a group of pesticides called neonicotinoids some years ago. These were systemic pesticides that were absorbed into growing plants so that when aphids and other crop pests ate the leaves, they ingested these poisons and were paralysed and fell off the crop. The poisons also occurred in the pollens and nectars of the flowers of the crops too and

White ermine moth

caused the same harmful effects to visiting pollinating insects – particularly bees. It was a victory for wildlife when these poisons were banned. And although countries can still make a case for a derogation if they maintain that a particular crop such as sugar beet cannot be protected in any other way, such derogations are rarely granted. We have not had any derogations in Ireland – so far. But in Britain, because of Brexit, they are no longer bound by such EU rules, so farmers can apply for derogations there, which are being granted in many cases.

Knowing what wildlife visits our local area – being able to put a name to a face, as it were – greatly increases our respect for them. If you know that bats are important consumers of insects such as moths that otherwise might be pests on crops, then you welcome a colony in your area. When you realise how many rats a pair of breeding barn owls consume in a season, then you are very inclined to put up the special barn owl breeding boxes around your farm to improve the chances of them patrolling your land at night for free. When you understand that poisons persist through the food chain, then you are more likely to make the connection between the loss of thrushes or hedgehogs in your area and the little blue pellets that you put out for the slugs and snails in your garden. There are non-poisonous ways of reducing their numbers if you care enough.

Wildlife species in a natural situation do not cause the extinction of other species. Unlikely as it might appear at first glance, the predator is controlled by the prey, not the other way round. No fox is ever going to kill every last rabbit – the strongest and the fittest survive, but when human-introduced myxomatosis decimated the rabbit population in the north-east of Ireland in the 1970s, the number of foxes crashed too as their principal food source had been removed. No, it really takes concerted human effort to make a species extinct as we did with sea eagles in the nineteenth century and golden eagles in 1912.

Therefore knowing what species visit your garden or your farm or your local park is the first step in understanding why they live there and the role they play in the whole ecosystem. Habitats with many different species, for instance those with high biodiversity, are indicators of a healthy and thriving natural environment. If we can't even identify a robin, the most fearless and friendly of our garden birds, how can we know whether the place is any good for wildlife or not? Surely we are not that bad yet in this country – or are we?

CHAPTER TEN

Lip Service is Not Enough

The summer of 2021 was the hottest summer Ireland ever had, with temperatures of over 30°C on several days, officially declared heatwaves and a shortage of water for crops and animals. And the thing is that it is quite likely to be the coolest summer this decade looking back, as we go through the decade and each summer gets hotter and hotter. Continental Europe really sweltered this year with temperatures of over 45°C in parts of France, Spain and Portugal, with persistent droughts and raging forest fires. There is no doubting it, climate change has led to this global warming. Other parts of the world such as India and Bangladesh have suffered from floods and landslides as the increased levels of carbon dioxide in our atmosphere traps more and more heat.

It is not a convenient time to be worrying about it. We have just come through two years of a pandemic that has not gone away either. We are learning to live with it and every effort is being made to mitigate its effects on the world's population. We are all in this together, we are told. Lockdown and self-isolation were hard to bear. We feel we are entitled to have a bit of leeway

Wind turbine at Bindoo Wind Farm, Greaghnacross, Co. Cavan

now – to travel abroad and receive visitors and see our friends after such an enforced separation.

The war in Ukraine has been waging since 24 February 2022. The effects of this are catastrophic for the Ukrainians forced to flee their homes. Economic restrictions have affected the distribution of food to the poorer parts of the world, already suffering from imminent famine because of crop failure. Restriction of fuel supplies will mean a difficult winter as the cost of heating our homes rises drastically.

We can't be thinking about climate change at the moment, and we certainly have enough to be putting up with, without further restrictions on how we live. Right?

No – not right. We are rapidly running out of time to take effective steps to halt and then reverse this climate change. There is no way that there is time for a break or for a holiday in our endeavours. As Irish people, we know this very well. Poll after poll has shown that we are very well aware of climate change, that we fully realise it is caused by human activity which increases the amount of carbon dioxide in the atmosphere – much more aware, for example, than the average American. But the thing is that while we know all this, we are actually quite reluctant to make changes in our own personal actions.

There are the usual excuses. What can one person do that will have any effect? We can't afford to make these big changes to our lifestyles. We don't want the reduced standard of living that we feel these changes will bring. Everyone will not have to make the same changes – only some of us – so why should it be us? Feeling like this deprives us of having any hope for the future and not having any hope for the future is unconscionable. Let's look at it with a positive approach.

Making positive change happen need not actually cost us any money. Each individual voice together can add up to quite a force when we really want something to change. Much of what Ireland can do in the fight against global warming is in changing how we produce electricity. We have the greatest resource in Europe for making electricity – not fossil fuels such as gas, oil and coal which we are using now, but wind. We have vast amounts of offshore wind available to us in our part of the Atlantic Ocean. The technology is there to build offshore floating anchored wind turbines that would harness far greater amounts of wind over the ocean than ever blow over the land. But, because of the ways things are done or not done in Ireland, it will take at least seven years to get even one turbine operational, starting from now. Why are we putting up with this? Such a lengthy process does not happen in other countries. One voice, together with all the other voices, clamouring for this could effect change if we badger every politician that we encounter. Solar farms, amazingly in what we have always perceived as a cold cloudy island, are also now a going concern in generating electricity from renewable resources. Both wind and sun are limitless and free. There is no dependence on other countries for continued supply. Why are we not shouting from the rooftops for this to start at once instead of lodging objections when any of these might be planned for anywhere near where we live?

Recent figures have shown that 4 million single-use coffee cups are binned every single week in Ireland (if they are lucky!). Many of them do not actually make the bin at all, but instead are thrown on footpaths, roadside verges, beaches and waterways. What are we like? There are only 5 million of us in the country, we don't all drink coffee by any means. Apparently 70 per cent

of coffee drinkers have keep cups, which they can have filled with coffee by the vendor, but most of us don't use them. But surely recycling the coffee cups is the answer. If we carefully put the empties into the recycling bin, sure aren't we grand? Well, no, actually. A recyclable coffee cup is not just made from paper – if it was, the paper would get saturated with the hot coffee and leak. They are lined with plastic. In the case of the recyclable ones, the plastic is a bioplastic made from plants – not mineral oil – and so it is compostable. But the plants used to make bioplastic are maize and sugar cane – plants that are a source of food too. It is mad to think that we would use this food resource to make a single-use coffee cup. If all the coffee cups in the world were changed to be lined with compostable bioplastic, more than half of all the maize grown in the world would be used for this. This would be an insane use of 60 million hectares of agricultural land.

We all know about the three Rs: Reduce, Reuse and Recycle. There is a fourth R which is much more important than any of the other three – Refuse. Refuse to be part of this unjustifiable waste of the world's already strained resources. You can still have your coffee to go but bring your own cup. Encourage your friends to do the same thing. Buy a keep cup as a present the next time you have to give a gift. Remember when we abolished plastic carrier bags in supermarkets and made people pay for them or bring their own reusable one? That started here in Ireland and now it is the norm in many other countries. We can't imagine not bringing our shopping bags now; we can do the same with coffee cups and we will feel very pleased with ourselves when we do.

It is not hopeless … yet. All is not yet lost. But we have to do more than just pay lip service. We have to show that we are willing to do things that make a difference, to encourage others to do the same. Even more importantly, we have to stop objecting to big plans because we don't like the look of them, or because they spoil our view. It used to be the story that our grandchildren would suffer and many of us thought, maybe subliminally, that we wouldn't be around to have to look them in the eye and explain why we stood idly by and let it happen. The timescale is shorter now. It is to our children that we will have to tender feeble and inadequate reasons for why we failed to act while there was still time.

CHAPTER ELEVEN

Noblesse Oblige.
With Power Comes Responsibilities

I was elected President of An Taisce in 2004, a voluntary unpaid position of this NGO that was founded by Robert Lloyd Praeger in 1948. Back then he made a radio address explaining what this new organisation was about. *Taisce* is the Irish word for treasure, for something very dear to one. For example, a mother might call her precious child *a thaisce* when speaking endearingly. The new organisation was founded to protect 'things of natural beauty' in Ireland. Praeger elaborated on what was involved – the provision of open spaces, the prevention of disfigurement of Irish towns and the countryside by injudicious building and the preservation of places for our native population of animals and plants. 'Our goal is a noble one,' he went on to say, 'and once it is fully appreciated, there is little reason that anyone's hand should be turned against us.'

But there's the rub – once it is fully appreciated. Almost seventy-five years later, can we truly say that the importance of what Praeger called 'things of natural beauty', and what we call today natural habitats and biodiversity, are fully appreciated? I got my eyes opened very quickly when I became President of An

The Royal Canal near Phibsborough, Dublin, with Croke Park stadium in the distance

Taisce. The work of An Taisce was absolutely fine with everyone when it involved setting up and running the very successful Green Flag Scheme for schools. Over 90 per cent of our primary schools today proudly fly Green Flags, as do many of our post-primary schools as well – the work of their pupils in increasing environmental awareness being of a high enough standard to achieve these European Standard Flags.

Another big project that An Taisce worked on in the 1970s was the restoration of the Royal Canal, which could certainly be described as protecting a thing of natural beauty by the thousands today who use both the canal banks and the once more fully-functioning waterway, for recreation and amenity.

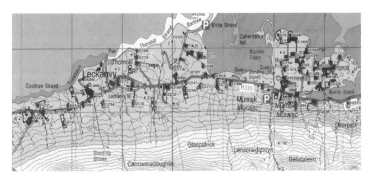

Map of Mayo

But it was the role An Taisce had in the planning process that caused heads to be turned against it.

Until the 1960s in Ireland, anyone could build anything anywhere or indeed knock down and destroy existing buildings with impunity. But the 1963 Local Government (Planning and Development) Act required that from then on permission must be acquired for such activities. The planning section of each local authority granted, or refused, these permissions. There were four prescribed authorities named in the legislation that were entitled to comment on proposed developments in sensitive areas – Bord Fáilte, The National Monuments Advisory Council, the Arts Council and An Taisce.

Comment, mind – not give or refuse planning permission. None of the prescribed authorities could ever do that. The planners had to give consideration to their comments but were not under an obligation to act on them. An Taisce took this role very seriously and made comments on developments that it considered were injurious to the environment, as it was invited to do under the legislation.

Mount Brandon, Co. Kerry

So, what is needed when someone wants to build a house in modern-day Ireland? Among other things, the house must have access to a clean supply of water and must be able to get rid of dirty water and sewage. Connection to the electricity network, and increasingly nowadays internet and broadband access, is seen as essential. Access to tarred roads on which vehicles can drive goes without saying. It would also seem to go without saying that these should all be acquirable without causing harm to anyone. And these are among the considerations made by the planners when looking at applications for planning permission for proposed development.

It is clear enough in areas where a population of people already live, for example, in a town or village. Clean water provided by the council is piped to the houses in the area and there are mains pipes to take away and treat the sewage and dirty water. There is an already existing electricity grid and mobile phone coverage and broadband is either there or at least about to be rolled out in the not so distant future. If the centre of population is big enough, not only are there excellent roads, but there is the possibility of public transport too and shops and schools nearby, thus lessening the dependence on motor cars, most of which burn fossil fuels.

A proposed isolated one-off house in a remote rural area needs all these facilities too but providing them may not be so clear-cut. New poles may be needed to bring the electricity. A new mast may be needed to get the mobile signal to the remote area where the new house is proposed. There may be no water pipes from the council with clean water or mains to take away the sewage. But all is not lost – a well can be sunk for drinking water and a septic tank constructed to cope with the waste water and sewage.

Septic tanks are wonderful things. Properly constructed and maintained, the bacteria in the soakaway area break down waste organic matter – to put it politely – seven litres at a time, which is the volume of a toilet cistern. In the right soil conditions these bacteria clean the dirty water before it sinks down to the ground water level – the level from which the clean water for the well is drawn. But if the soil conditions are not right, this won't happen. If the soil is too light and sandy, the dirty water soaks down too quickly, carrying its load of harmful germs to the groundwater. If the soil is too clayey it is even worse because the soakaway times are far too long, the dirty water pools in the soil and the bacteria that should be breaking down the organic material cannot function in the oxygen-deprived waterlogged soil. And that is before the householder takes it into their head to pour volumes of bleach into the toilet to kill 'all-known germs' – meaning the good useful soakaway bacteria are soon rendered extinct.

Water from a well sunk down into groundwater contaminated by sewage is unsafe. The Galway people who tried to go back to their wells for drinking water when the treatment plant at Terryland got contaminated with cryptosporidium from Lough

Corrib – the source of its water – soon found this out. They were still depending on septic tanks, but clean water had subsequently been piped to them over the years by the council until this pollution incidence happened. It took months to sort out and the wells could not be put back into service because these tanks had contaminated the groundwater that was their source.

So when, in the most egregious of cases, An Taisce would comment that the soil on which a house was proposed to be built was such that a septic tank would cause groundwater pollution, damaging the local environment and probably contaminating groundwater from which wells were being fed, this was considered to be busybody interference, and it was argued that such comments and objections should be withdrawn at once. I spent five years as President of An Taisce pointing out that development that damaged the environment was not in the public interest. An Taisce was founded by Praeger seventy-five years ago as an organisation that would defend the natural and the built environment. A worthy sentiment indeed, as long as it remained just a general vague woolly aspiration, it would seem. In actual fact, there are approximately half a million houses with septic tanks in Ireland out of a total of two million houses, so they are not a vanishing species. Whether they all operate safely and never contaminate ground water, well *sin scéal eile*.

CHAPTER TWELVE

Christmas Wildlife

Lots of different wildlife species form part of our Christmas celebrations. Some are recent customs, while others date from thousands of years ago. It is interesting to examine the background to all this as it gives more meaning to the customs.

Take robins for example. Why are there robins on Christmas cards? This is indeed a good question seeing as how robins are terribly belligerent birds and can't bear other robins around except during the breeding season when they tolerate a mate on their territory. So when we send Christmas cards wishing each other peace and happiness, why do we sometimes choose cards with these belligerent robins on them? It all goes back to Victorian England when the postal system was first set up. The postmen then wore red uniforms and were thus nicknamed robins. They were represented as robins on the Christmas cards that they delivered.

As discussed in Chapter Eight, the wren is also associated with this time of year. Capturing the wren is a tradition that stems from this tiny bird's betrayal of Stephen, who became the first Christian martyr. The story goes that St Stephen was captured

Mistletoe, Botanic Gardens, Dublin

and murdered by Roman soldiers as he tried to sneak past them as they slept. The soldiers woke up when a wren hopped up and down on their drum.

But some seem to think that the tradition is much older than this, dating from the Bronze Age and the new year ceremonies of the Neolithic farmers. Others say that the wren was always a sneaky bird anyway. It is supposed to be the king of the birds because it hitched a ride on the back of the eagle when the birds were having a competition to see who could fly the highest. When the eagle could fly no higher, the wren hopped out from under its feathers and flew above it, thus claiming the title.

Indeed, the tradition of the wren boys is still followed on St Stephen's Day in parts of Ireland, but catching and killing wrens no longer has a part in it. Like all our garden birds, wrens are fully protected under our wildlife legislation.

Reindeer feature too, as they pull Santy's sleigh around the world on Christmas Eve. We have three species of deer in Ireland – red deer, sika deer and fallow deer. But did we ever actually have reindeer here? They were a native species at the end of the last Ice Age ten thousand years ago. When the ice covering Ireland receded, the slowly warming country was covered with tundra-like vegetation with poor thin soils on which grasses and lichens grew. Great herds of reindeer and indeed great Irish deer roamed the uninhabited countryside. We know this from remains of bones dug up in bogs or found in caves. But the country continued to warm up and the tundra grasslands were replaced by temperate forests that covered the whole place. The reindeer moved further north over land bridges that are long since gone. The great Irish deer did not fare so well. They stayed too long and became extinct, as, with their enormous antlers, they could not survive in the dense woodlands. A skeleton of a great Irish deer can be seen in the Natural History Museum in Dublin.

The reindeer still thrive today in Tundra regions further north – in Finland, Lapland and in northern Canada, where they are known as caribou. But of course, Rudolph and Olive (the other reindeer) always lead Santy's team of reindeer across Ireland on Christmas Eve.

Certain plants form part of our Christmas celebrations too. The holly and the ivy are mentioned in Christmas carols. We bring them in to decorate our houses at Christmas. The holly traditionally was put behind the pictures and in our house, certainly, the ivy formed part of the roofing material for the crib. Some people think that this is a Christian tradition – that the prickles on the holly bring to mind the crown of thorns that Jesus wore, while the red berries remind us of his blood. But the tradition is way older than that.

It dates from Neolithic times when the earliest farmers relied entirely on the sun and on daylight for their crops and herds. They built places like Newgrange, where the lowest point the sun reached in the sky could be measured. I am sure they watched with great concern on the days after the solstice to see would the sun start to move higher again in the sky rather than continue its slow descent and perhaps vanish altogether. When it could be definitely ascertained that the sun was moving higher again, there was great rejoicing that the sun god Lugh had not abandoned them. They rushed into the woods to gather any living plant to bring indoors to celebrate that life would continue. In those native deciduous forests long ago, holly and ivy were two of the few plants in leaf at that time and so were borne joyfully indoors. And we are still doing it!

Robin

They brought in mistletoe in other European countries, because it too is an evergreen and magically – it seemed – was in full leaf on leafless trees such as oak. It is semi-parasitic on these trees and remains in leaf throughout the winter. It is not native here and was not included in our traditional Christmas customs until very recently.

Christmas trees are a fairly recent thing as well. Bringing a whole tree indoors was a middle European tradition. There, conifers are native in the woodlands and were brought in to celebrate the return of the light. When Charlotte left her native Germany to marry King George III in the 1790s, she introduced this custom to Britain. But it took Queen Victoria's German-born husband, Albert, to really popularise them there. An engraving he organised of the royal family standing around a beautifully decorated Christmas tree in 1848 went viral, as it were, and the good citizens of Britain and North America couldn't wait to have one too. It was at least another century before they became popular here.

So when we continue carrying on our Christmas traditions, it is good to know why we do so.

CHAPTER THIRTEEN

All Things Bright and Beautiful. Biodiversity – What Did It Ever Do For Us?

We are well into spring. Six weeks before and six weeks after the vernal equinox, which this year falls on 20 March 2023, is when the season of spring is – no matter what anyone says about it starting on the first day of March. The lengthening days are not affected by global climate change and 1 February is the first day of spring regardless of what the thermometer reads.

Nature is inexorably stirring. The fact that the days are lengthening is noted by many of our wild animals. The pineal gland that almost all vertebrate species, including ourselves, have registers the increasing duration of daylight and affects behaviour. Our plants are reacting too. The sap is rising in the trees – you can sometimes even hear it if you press your ear against the trunk. But are we still noticing as many species of plants and animals this year as in other years and are the numbers of each species as great as before?

For that is what biodiversity means. This word was only coined in the 1980s and is a combination of two perfectly understandable words – bio meaning life and diversity meaning variation. Biodiversity is the variety of all living things; the

Round-leaved sundew

different plants, animals and microorganisms, the genetic information they contain and the ecosystems they form. So, the greater the number of different species of creatures and plants that we see around us, the better is the biodiversity in our area.

But does it matter? In the great scheme of things does it really matter if only three species of birds come to our feeding station in the garden instead of ten? If there are only one or two species of trees and bushes in the hedge around the field instead of fifteen? How is it going to affect us?

It goes back to the whole idea of a food chain. Plants are the only producers of food on earth. They do this by photosynthesis – turning the carbon part of the carbon dioxide in the air into carbon sugars such as glucose, while using sunlight for energy. These simple sugars are then modified in plants into more complicated sugars and starches as well as proteins and oils. Thus, the plants feed all the animal life in the world including ourselves, either directly as vegetable food or further along the food chain, as food for animals then eaten by others. The more variation there is in plants, then the greater variety of animal life that can be supported.

This can be very obvious in our gardens in spring. Queen bumblebees come out of hibernation now and set about building a nest, laying eggs and founding new colonies. There must be food to enable them to do this – nectar to feed themselves and pollen to feed the little baby bees when they hatch out. Lots of different species of plants in the area mean that many of the early ones will be in flower and contain the vital nectar and pollen that they need. But not if the garden is full of daffodils and early tulips. These flowers, so beloved of gardeners, are entirely propagated through bulbs. They contain neither pollen nor nectar useful for insects – they form no seeds. Native spring flowers such as dandelions, primroses, bluebells, hazel and willow catkins are great sources of food – even garden flowers such as crocuses, grape hyacinths and snowdrops have useful food too. Bumblebees are not the only insects to depend on nectar in their adult stages either – so fewer nectar-bearing flower species mean fewer insect species.

There is no biodiversity in humans. We are the most numerous vertebrate species on earth, all eight billion of us now, but we are all the same species. There is very little biodiversity in our food either since we stopped being hunter-gatherers ten thousand years ago and came to depend on farming to feed us. Three-quarters of the world's food supply depends on just twelve plant species. In fact, more than half of our food worldwide comes from just three plants – wheat, rice and maize. In order to grow the great quantities of these that are needed, areas with great biodiversity of plants and animals are swept clear. The monoculture is planted and kept free from any animal and insect predators by the use of pesticides. Even in Ireland, 50 per cent of our land is given over to growing grass – and only one or two species at that, which are the most nourishing for the livestock that eat it. Not much biodiversity in that half of Ireland.

But does it matter as long as we have enough to eat? Of course it does. Clearing land for agriculture destroys the natural ecosystems that were there before. In order to have great biodiversity of plant and animal species, there must be great biodiversity of ecosystems too. By reducing the native deciduous woodlands in Ireland from 80 per cent cover when humans came here first, to about 2 per cent cover at the beginning of the last century, we made extinct here a great deal

Moss, ivy, grass and ferns, Co. Roscommon

of plants, insects, birds and mammals that depended on these areas in order to live. It will be the same when we finally burn and drain the last of our bogs. We have regulations in place to prevent this happening, but they are continually flouted. As well as this, in 2022 as Minister Eamon Ryan explained in the Dáil, we exported 500,000 tonnes of peat, mainly for horticultural purposes, extracted without any planning permission being either sought or granted. Biodiverse ecosystems buffer us from natural disasters such as floods and storms, filter our water and protect our soils. The mangrove areas around the coasts of the countries in South-East Asia are increasingly being cleared to farm those freshwater prawns that are sent thousands of airmiles to the shelves of the supermarkets of Europe and the US. And those countries, stripped of their protective ecosystems, are increasingly at risk from floods and sea-level rises.

The more we destroy natural habitats, the closer we live to the remaining wildlife. It is becoming more common for diseases that previously only affected wildlife to make the leap and mutate into human diseases with the potential to turn into pandemics. All our medicines come originally from plants. Chemists are able to identify and chemically synthesise the active ingredient – for example, salicylic acid from the bark of willow trees, the active ingredient in aspirin. By destroying vast swathes of hugely biodiverse tropical rainforest, we also destroy who knows how many potential sources of life-improving medicines.

One might be tempted to think it serves us right for behaving in this way. But there is a deeper and more fundamental reason not to destroy biodiversity, but instead to seek out ways to co-exist with it and actively strive to improve and increase it. We are but one species on planet earth. How can it be morally justified to wantonly decimate the other species we share the earth with and to destroy the ecosystems where they live, just for our own greed? It's not as if we need freshwater prawns from the other side of the world or strawberries in January.

We are causing a worldwide biodiversity crisis mainly through rapidly changing land use. In the past fifty years – since the 1970s – we have presided over a 70 per cent loss of vertebrate wildlife worldwide. Not a 70 per cent loss of species but a reduction of 70 per cent in the actual number of individual tigers and herrings and gorillas, to name but a few.

In Ireland, the recent publication *Plant Atlas 2020: Mapping Changes in the Distribution of the British and Irish Flora* shows that there has been a 56 per cent decline in Ireland's native wild plants since the 1950s. Many of our animals and birds are faring badly too. There has been a catastrophic reduction of over 90 per cent in breeding curlews and corncrakes, wild Irish salmon are almost a thing of the past and when was the last time you saw a hedgehog?

Afterword

In the foregoing series of chapters I have been musing on the state of our planet and the reasons for it being in this state. I haven't pulled any punches, and readers might come to the conclusion that I don't hold out much hope for our natural world. Nothing could be further from the truth. What I base my optimism on is the fact that as humans have caused this deterioration, then so too can they reverse the trend. Many of the difficulties encountered by our fellow travellers on spaceship earth are caused by land-use change. This has happened bit by bit over the past ten thousand years – death by a thousand cuts, as it were. We are more likely to think that it is within all our powers to reverse this trend – more so perhaps than we can address the enormous behemoth that is climate change. Of course, changing land use causes climate change – it adds to greenhouse gas emissions when bogs are drained and turf is cut, or when forests are replaced with nitrate-enriched fields supporting just two grass species. Europe was once covered in temperate forests which held on to the carbon their trees had removed from the atmosphere, as indeed the tropical rainforests still do – what are left of them. But somehow we feel empowered by thinking that the ability to stop this adverse land-use change lies in the hands of those of us who own the land, right down to the smallest garden patch.

Knowledge is power. Never was there so much known about the state of our natural environment and indeed what and who has reduced it to this state. The instinct of self-preservation is the strongest human instinct. I cannot see it failing now. Children and grandchildren confer immortality on us. It is still in our capability to have a liveable planet for them.

Acknowledgements

This book came into existence as result of a great deal of willing assistance. It began life as a series of articles in the magazine *Intercom*, commissioned by the editor, Paul Clayton-Lea. He gave me a brief to write about our natural world, our responsibility for the state of it and how we were living up to these responsibilities. Thank you, Paul. Síne Quinn, publisher at Beehive Books, had the idea of putting together a year of these articles as a book and how it now looks between covers is thanks to herself and to Colette Dower, Production/Design & Typesetting Manager, who did the design and typesetting. The photographs add to it and I am very grateful to the Tree Council of Ireland, Terry Flanagan and Maebh Harding who allowed me to use some of theirs without making any bones about it. Thanks also to Natasha Mac a'Bháird for proofing the final text and also to Jack Carey, Fiona Dunne and all the team at Beehive Books.

I particularly want to thank Michael Fewer for his erudite and generous foreword. Manchán Magan and Róisín Ingle have been extremely generous in their praise of the results – thanks to both of you for your paeans of praise.